PITFALL

by
BARBARA HALLIHAN

1974

Published by Zoar Publications, Sheffield,

CONTENTS

© First Published 1972

ISBN: 0 904435 05 9

CHAPTER ONE

Home

No one could call Peter Morrison's village beautiful; the most noticeable colour was — black! The few straggly hawthorn trees and hedges, which lay on the outskirts of the village all wore a thin film of black over the greenness; the houses which huddled together as if for company were dirty and uncared for; the road, which had no tarmac in those days, was black; everywhere there were enormous mounds of black dust with a few poor sickly clumps of grass struggling to cover up the ugliness; even the streams seemed to be carrying thick black cream, and what birds there were, mostly sparrows, looked as dirty and unloved as the houses.

What a place to live in! Yet this poor place had an important part to play, for it was here that coal was mined. In Psalm 104, verse 24, it is written: " . . . the earth is full of Thy riches," and so it is. There were plenty of riches known when that was written, but there have been many more discovered since then, and one of these is coal, or "black diamonds" as it is sometimes called.

The people who lived in Peter's village were, at one time, as ugly and dirty as the houses and streets. They lived each day as if God did not exist, and Sundays were days in which to drink too much beer and to do all the things they had not had time for during the other six days. But though they pushed God out of their thoughts, God had not neglected them, for He sent Gospel preachers into the village, and by the time Peter was fourteen there were many who had been made into new creatures in Christ Jesus. Even those who were not born again were quieter, and were a little restrained in their wickednesses.

Peter Morrison's mother was a Christian; she had never been to school and therefore she did not know many things, but she knew how to read. The one book she read and enjoyed most was her Bible, and she had need of the strength to be found from God's Word, because Mr. Morrison had died when Peter was only five years old and his little sister Mary was only three. However, she was strong and she worked hard to keep the children well fed and clothed, until Peter was old enough to work. In the nineteenth century this was very early, and he was not much more than nine when he first went, as his father had done, down the mine.

Peter's home was a cottage in a row built near the coalmine. At a quick glance, the outside of the houses were all the same, very small, with tiny windows and bricks covered in black coal dust. Here and there were differences, though; gleaming windows, with no broken panes, clean paintwork and clean curtains at the windows, contrasting with shattered glass and dirty rags stuffed into the holes. Peter's home was one of these bright clean ones, and the inside, though tiny, was as clean as a new pin. There were two rooms downstairs, one was a living room, with polished furniture and a bright rag rug on the stone floor, giving a splash of warm colour. By the big kitchen range was a bookshelf on which their small collection of precious books was kept: Mr. Morrison's small Bible, worn and grimy from being carried in his pocket so long, but which was kept as a reminder of a loved father, Pilgrim's Progress, two or three hymn books, for the family liked to sit round the fire in the evenings sometimes and sing their favourite hymns, and one or two other much fingered books, and in the middle of the sideboard a large strongly bound family Bible. This book was truly the centre of Peter's home, not as something only to look at, but the Book which guided the family through all its difficulties and hard times. The second room downstairs was a bedroom for Mrs. Morrison and Mary. Up a narrow staircase was a large loft lit by two little windows in the roof; here Peter slept, and here he often sat in summer evenings by an open window, dreaming, or reading what books he could lay his hands on.

CHAPTER TWO

Sunday

Six o'clock, and the sun sent a long bright finger through Peter's window and touched his face just as he opened his eyes. Without thinking, he leapt out of bed and began feeling for his clothes. Then he remembered and relaxed; today was not a working day and he had not overslept, for today was Sunday, his happiest day.

"Good," he thought, "I can have another hour," and he moved to settle himself down again, when a verse from his hymnbook came into his mind, "This is the day that Christ arose so early from the dead; Why should I then my eyelids close and waste my hours in bed?" Another look at the bed tempted him

4

to slide in, but with an effort he stayed on his feet and began dressing. Now he was actually up, it would be silly to go back and try to make himself sleepy again. Instead he enjoyed the relief of dressing in clean Sunday clothes, in place of his working clothes smelling of the coal.

By seven, Peter, Mary and Mrs. Morrison were having their breakfast. After the table was cleared, Mrs. Morrison moved the big Bible on to the table and the children sat beside her. She read her favourite Psalm, number 91, because it speaks of God's faithfulness to those who put their trust in Him. Peter chose the exciting story of Elijah on Mount Carmel, when God confounded the priests of Baal, and Mary chose the amazing story of how the baby Moses was not only saved from death but even had his own mother to look after him. Mrs. Morrison prayed for God's blessing on them and their doings that day, then sent the children off to Sunday School before the morning service.

It was a lovely summer morning, and even in this dirty place, the sun shone clean and bright. Here and there men sat on their doorsteps while lots of grubby children played up and down the streets, getting grubbier. As Peter and Mary were passing a group of boys, one of them, Jos Hartley, shouted, "Hi, Peter, come with us, we're going for a long walk through the fields." He knew how much Peter loved the countryside, for while they had been at school together they had had many a day on the moors. "If I were you, I wouldn't keep going to Sunday School; haven't you had enough of it, I have." "No, I haven't," Peter replied, "I like it."

"You only like it because you must," Jos said scornfully, "You only go because your mother sends you." Now this stung Peter; he and Jos worked together in the mine, and to be teased with being a mammy's boy when he was a breadwinner was hard to bear.

"My mother doesn't **make** me go to Sunday School," he replied hotly, "I go because it's interesting."

"Doesn't she, though," Jos said, not because he was an unpleasant boy, but because he could not think of anything more convincing to say! He and Peter enjoyed a sort of companionship which sprang from their work together, but the main difference was that Jos's parents were not Christians, and Sunday was just another day to them, when the children had to keep out of the way while the work went on as usual. Peter was sorely tried by the desire to spend a fine day on the moor, for the sun did shine brightly, but he found he could not give in and deceive his mother, so he grabbed Mary by the arm and hustled her down the street flinging a "Please yourself" to Jos as they passed.

So Sunday passed for Peter as each preceding Sunday passed, and the day closed with Peter and Mary and Mrs. Morrison feeling refreshed in spirit and body, and ready for another week of hard work. Not so Jos. He had had his walk through the fields, and other hectic activities, finishing with a cock fight. He crawled home worn out, only wanting to sleep and to forget that tomorrow was Monday.

6

CHAPTER THREE

A Working Day

It was not absolutely dark as Peter went downstairs
to put his work clothes on, for the sun was peeping
over the moors. He hurried his breakfast down, picked
up his day's sandwiches, paused while his mother
briefly commended him to the Lord's safe keeping, as
she always did, then raced out to join the stream of
men and boys hurrying to work. When he reached the
large hole in the ground which was the mouth of the
pit, men were already being lowered, most of them in
the large basket which travelled up and down on a
thick chain; others went down by means of a looped
rope; it was possible for two to travel in this way, by
putting one leg each through the loop and holding

7

tight to the rope with both hands. It sounds hair raising but Peter had done it so often that he no longer thought anything about it. The shaft was about six feet square, shored up by great pieces of timber, and as Peter and Jos travelled down they watched the square of light get smaller and smaller as the darkness closed round them. Now the only lights were the small safety lamps which each miner carried. At the bottom of the shaft, Peter and Jos climbed from the rope and set off along the big wide passage, or gallery, which led to their place of work. As they passed along the gallery, they saw the smaller "workings", the galleries at right angles to the main one, where the coal was being hewed out and put into tubs on wheels called corves. All these passages were criss-crossed by other low tramways along which the corves ran, to bring the coal to the foot of the shaft. These passages, for safety reasons had to be kept closed, but the doors or traps had to be opened constantly to let the corves through. At each door there was a little cave hollowed out of the wall in which sat a little boy or sometimes a girl, whose sole duty was to open the trap when he heard a corve rumbling along the rails, and to let it drop shut afterwards. This was the job that most children began with as they did not need to be strong, and this was how Peter had begun his working life when he was nine, sitting in his little cave from four in the morning until six at night. His next work when he was stronger was to push or pull the corves along, and it was in this work that he was paired with Jos Hartley. Together they trudged backwards and forwards with corves, full ones slowly to the foot of the shaft, and speeding back

with the empty ones. But it was monotonous work, and they looked forward to the time when they would be promoted to hewers and actually cut out the coal for others to load.

Finishing time came at last, and the boys made their way to the bottom of the shaft, waiting their turn to be drawn up to the daylight and fresh air. At home, Peter's first job was always to wash and change his clothes. While he was so dust-encrusted all day, it was a pleasure to be clean and tidy before sitting down to supper with Mary and his mother. Even though there was still some daylight outside, Peter was too tired to do anything but climb up to his loft to fall fast asleep. Outside, as the darkness slowly deepened, the village fell silent and lights went out one by one. Soon, all that could be seen were the tall chimneys belching out flaming smoke where the furnaces burnt, driving the machinery which brought the coal up.

CHAPTER FOUR

Earth-fall!

Tuesday began as every Tuesday began, and Peter and Jos were at their usual work, singing as they pushed empty corves, puffing and grunting as they heaved full ones along.

Suddenly—as they were returning to the working with an empty corve, they heard a noise which sounded like a clap of thunder, and miners' lamps were blown out by choking clouds of dust carried along on a great gust of air. The older miners knew only too well what that noise meant, and it struck terror into their hearts. Somewhere, a roof was caving in and tons of earth were pouring down to block galleries and passages

Then, from all over the mine came the hewers, trappers and others running as quickly as they could to the shaft to be brought to safety. They were quickly hauled to the surface, and a count was taken to see who was missing. Jos Hartley, Peter Morrison, two hewers James Freeman and Bill Logan, and a little trapper Bobby Lester did not answer their names when called. Already crowds of anxious mothers, wives and children were gathering at the pithead calling out for their menfolk, and crying with relief when they found them safe and well. Except for one little group of white-faced, stricken women and children, those who had no menfolk waiting for them. It seemed impossible to them that anyone could still be alive, for the men nearest the fall described the terrible sound as the earth fell in.

Those men who had run for their lives were no cowards, and now some stepped forward to go down and find out if anyone had survived. About twenty men, with the mine manager, were lowered to the bottom. As they shone their lamps around, their hearts sank; the gallery where the missing team had been was choked by the masses of rock and earth and broken roof timbers, and all this hung in such a way as if a sneeze might start another avalanche down on the rescuers' heads. As they looked, they knew that if anyone had been underneath the rocks, they could not now be alive, but there was an alternative. Perhaps the roof had only fallen part way along the gallery and the team were unharmed further on. If this were so, even then they were not safe, for the dangers to be faced were starvation or suffocation if the air supply was cut off. Each case seemed hopeless; but not being fair weather friends only, they determined to work for their mates' rescue until they were delivered or their own strength failed.

With this determination they set to work with proper tools to clear a way through the fall of rock. What hazards surrounded them! It seemed every moment that they must be crushed by a fresh fall; then a new trouble appeared—water began to pour over them and continued to rise until it was up to their knees. They carried on working, thinking only of the trapped men and boys and their grieving families, and though bathed in sweat, nigh dropping with weariness, they toiled on. Pumps were arranged to keep the water down, and fresh air was pumped along. Before nightfall news of the disaster had spread to other villages and men came flocking from other pits to help. Help was sorely needed, and to keep the work going and to ease the burden, fresh teams kept coming to relieve those below. It seemed work in vain, for they had called and called as they worked, but had heard no sign that there was any life.

Then suddenly, one said "Hush, stop and listen." They listened, holding their breath; then far off, so faint, they heard: clink, clink, clink, clink, clink. Five times. A silence—then again, clink, clink, clink, clink, clink; a silence — and again five more taps. Immediately, with the quickness of thought granted in such a situation, the men interpreted that as meaning that the trapped people were alive — all five! The

rescuers raised a cheer and set to work with fresh zeal, and when their turn came to return to the surface, they were able to take more hopeful news to the relatives who kept watch.

CHAPTER FIVE

What Lies Ahead?

What of Peter and his companions? He and Jos had been saved from death by arriving at the working with their empty corve seconds before the roof fell. As for Bobby Lester, the little trapper, he had been sitting by his door when the rumbling began and his terror drove him to run to the two men James Freeman and Bill Logan, thus he too was saved from being crushed. The two men kept enough control over themselves to make the boys stand quietly with them until all the noise and trembling had ceased. Then Bill Logan crept down the passage to discover how bad the fall was. His mates waited what seemed an age for his return, and one look at his face when he did showed them that things were serious. In a voice husky with feeling he said simply, "We're shut in — there's no way out into the gallery!" They heard him in silence, then Bobby cried piteously, "I want to go home, please let me go home." The realization that this was impossible brought tears to the men's eyes, and James Freeman answered very gently, "Yes, laddie, you shall go, just as soon as we find a way out, but you must wait a little while. You boys wait here and Logan and I will go see what can be done." They left a lighted lamp and went into the darkness.

They were gone longer this time, but their searchings were no more successful than before—they were well and truly shut in and buried alive! One mercy immediately apparent was that they were not short of fresh air; there must have been a small opening somewhere for it let in enough air to keep them comfortable. On their way back to the boys they collected their jackets and sandwiches which had been put aside when they began that morning. What had they to tell the boys, what comfort or hope could they give them? There seemed none. But—though these two men were poor, and had themselves gone down the mine when they were young and therefore had had little schooling, they had a source of comfort — they had read their Bibles, and with the help of the greatest of teachers, the Holy Spirit, they had learned of the love of the Lord Jesus Christ for sinners in need of salvation. They had been taught to look to Him for that eternal hope which is not affected by the things which happen on earth. Now, as they slowly walked back, Bill Logan said, "Well, James, what are we to do next?" James only shook his head sadly, and looked around with a feeling of helplessness. He was thinking of his wife and three children who must be in such distress. "There only seems to be one thing we can do," he answered, "You know where it is said 'Call upon me in the day of trouble: I will deliver thee and thou shalt glorify me.' That's a precious promise and tells us the thing we can do."

"That's right, James. We have done all we can for ourselves, and that's precious little, we must look to the Lord to help us. And we can be sure of this: God **is** able to deliver us if He sees fit, and if it pleases Him to take us to Himself from here, why, man, it's as near to heaven and glory at the bottom of a coal pit as anywhere."

They faced three anxious boys, and one such a little one. "Well, lads", Bill began, "we're in a terrible fix; there's no way round it so we must say it outright. There's nothing much of use we can do, but we can be sure that if anything can be done by others to help, it will be done. The only thing we can do to keep our hearts and courage up is to put our trust in Almighty God rather than men. Let's pray to Him now. He heard Jonah when he cried from the fish's belly down at the bottom of the sea, and He can hear us at the bottom of the mine. Come, lads." They knelt. Poor Bobby was sobbing with fear at such solemn words, and tears coursed quietly down the faces of the two older boys. Those two men then called upon God in their trouble, that it might please Him to deliver them from this trial, but if it was His will otherwise, then that they might **all** be prepared to stand before His throne.

How they prayed for all their families suffering so much distress on their behalf, and they pleaded that if they should not see them again on earth, that through the merits of the blessed Saviour they might meet them in glory. They also prayed for any other miners who might have been trapped in other parts of the mine, and lastly they pleaded for strength in their souls to bear their present affliction patiently, not charging God foolishly.

There was a heavy silence when the men finished. They rose from their knees, and already they felt the last part of their prayers answered, for their spirits rose also. Even little Bobby was now quiet and, though subdued, he was fairly cheerful. Peter felt so sure that help would come that he was already imagining his mother's and sister's happiness when he was brought out. The men, however, were more careful. They knew, better than the boys, just how long it might be before help reached them, if at all. They could not know how far the fall extended, they could not be sure the roof would not fall again, nor how they would live through days of waiting for the others to dig through to them. For these reasons they set themselves to take stock of their position. It was three or four hours since the fall, and they examined their supply of food. They had all managed to salvage their day's rations and so decided it was time for a meal.

"We'd better eat carefully," said James. "We ought to reckon on making what we've got last at least three days." "Three days!" exclaimed Jos in dismay. "Shall we not get out in less than three days?" He had shared

Peter's firm expectation of almost immediate release, so no wonder that his spirits dropped again.

"If it please the Lord, we may be released in a few hours," James replied, "but it's not likely, and we ought to be prepared for the worst. At any rate we ought to make our food hold out for three days if need be." Bobby had no appetite; the thought of being imprisoned for so long had raised all his fears and he would not eat. He had soon sobbed himself to sleep, he was so worn out, and James wrapped him up in his own jacket and laid him down comfortably. The rest soon finished their frugal meal and washed it down with a mouthful of beer from a bottle that Bill had had in his basket. This caused them to think of another serious question: it was possible that they could make their food last for three days—but what of drink? The bottle was already empty and it seemed more likely that they would suffer from thirst than from hunger. They were not troubled long, for they had scarcely packed away the rest of the food when they heard a dripping noise. After poking about a little, they discovered water dripping from the roof and trickling down the wall. This called the men's minds to the words, "When the poor and needy seek water, and there is none, and their tongue faileth for thirst, I the Lord will hear them, I the God of Israel will not forsake them."

Though they could not do much for their own release, it seemed right that they should try, so they got their tools and began cautiously to pick at the rubble. They soon found how useless their efforts were, for it slid and crumbled still more. They were giving

way to despair when a sound reached them that made their hearts beat quickly: it was a faint, faint sound of tools, but it was loud enough to reassure them that they were not forsaken, efforts were being made to release them. It occurred to one of the men to strike hard against the roof with his pickaxe, and we know how the signal was heard and understood!

All through the rest of that day the men and boys were very quiet. For the most part they listened to the comforting sounds of men working at the other side of the fall, and in calculating how many hours it might be before they would be free. As you can imagine, the hours passed slowly—so slowly, that Bill Logan, who carried a watch, often fancied it had stopped and it was only when he held it to his ear that its tick convinced him it still worked. But though time crept, that day did not pass too unhappily. There was the knowledge that help was coming, or at any rate they were not deserted by their workmates, and this filled them all, even Bobby, with hope. From time to time the two men spoke confidently of the providence of God over all, and of His especial goodness to those who trust in Him, that they cheered not only themselves, but the boys too. At length the watch told them it was night time, and after dividing some food up, and commending themselves again to Him who neither slumbers nor sleeps, they laid themselves down on the rough floor and slept.

It is more than likely that the prisoners slept more soundly that night than many in the village. The men who had been labouring all day did not sleep much for thinking of their buried fellows, and although they had said what they could to cheer the relatives, they had fears that help would be too late. There was little sleep, too, for the families: the wives and children of James Freeman and Bill Logan, the parents of Jos Hartley and young Bobby, and the mother and sister of Peter Morrison—they were all in too much sorrow to sleep. But if there was not much sleep there was much prayer. Many of those who had been hard at work during the day, instead of going straight to their own homes spent time together in prayer. So the night passed above ground, while others toiled on to open a way through the fall. When morning came these workers were relieved by others who had been resting.

All through the next two days and nights the workmen continued by turns their difficult and dangerous work, and every hour their difficulties increased. The hard rock they were trying to pierce seemed to become harder; sometimes the tools broke; at other times the passage which they had opened was closed by a fresh fall; then again, water which filtered in from all parts through the narrow gallery increased so much that they feared it would stop them altogether and they had to wait while it was pumped clear. And all this time there was the constant fear the whole roof would collapse and bury them all.

Among the rescuers was Bobby Lester's father. What agonies he suffered as he worked. Night and day he never left the mine and hardly left the work. If for a few minutes his strength failed, and he was forced to rest, he hurried back as soon as he was able to pick up his tools again. "Man, you'll kill yourself if you go on like this," said one of his mates with concern, "Leave us and rest, there's a good chap, and trust us to do all we can while you're gone." "No, no, Tom," Lester replied in a husky voice, "There's no child of yours in there. Mine is, and I'll not stop trying to save him. I promised his mother that we'd go out of this pit together, and so we will if it please God." He wiped tears away, which washed white channels down his rough dust-caked face, and again attacked the barrier which separated him from his boy. There was one occasional sound which brought hope to his heart and strength to his arms to keep going: that faint clink of iron against rock, five times repeated that told him that the lad still lived.

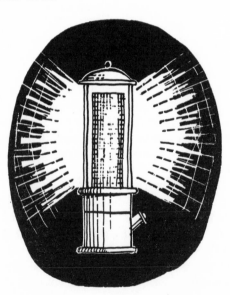

CHAPTER SIX

Jos Thinks!

"Do you think we'll get out of this, Peter?" asked Jos Hartley in a despondent voice. On the morning after the fall, the boys were sitting together, while the two men were searching in the vain hope of finding a way out which they might have missed.

"I don't know, Jos. I just don't know what to think."

"Peter, I wish—." Jos stopped.

"What do you wish?" Jos hesitated, then burst out with a rush, "I wish I hadn't gone where I did last Sunday. It's dreadful to be shut up here, and what if we should never get out!"

"I hope we shall Jos, they're working very hard for us, you know."

"Aye, but before they get at us we may be dead, or another fall may come."

The truth of this caused Peter's courage to crumble a little, especially when he thought of his mother and Mary. He was only able to answer, "We must keep up our hearts and hope, as Mr. Logan says, and think of good things."

"I don't know any good things to think about," Jos said moodily.

"I think you do, Jos, a few."

"I reckon I don't, then!"

"Not about the Bible, and about Jesus Christ? Jos, you **have** heard of Him, and how He came into the world to save sinners, and about His being crucified, dead and buried and then how He rose again and went up to Heaven. You know all about those things."

"Well, so what?" said Jos, weary and dispirited.

"Why these are good things for us," Peter answered, brightening up. "You know what the Bible says?"

Jos made no reply, and Peter, feeling discouraged, fell silent.

Presently Jos broke the silence again.

"I wish you would talk, Peter, it's very dismal in the dark."

Peter felt it was dismal too. Not that they were unused to being in the dark, but there is a difference between being at work in the dark, with a way open to the light, and being shut in and buried—alive. Peter was very willing to fight off the dreariness by talking, but what could he say? He could think of many things, but because of the differences between him and Jos, he feared he would not care to hear them, so he said,

"You talk, you're the eldest. Where did you go last Sunday that makes you wish you hadn't?"

Jos muttered that it didn't matter, he would rather not tell. Yet he did tell, for he wanted to get it off his mind. He'd gone roaming around the countryside with his friends. They had taken him to a cock-fight, then they had finished the day at a public house, making it extremely late when they got home.

"You should have been with Mother and Mary and me," Peter said, "you'd have heard a rare sermon."

"Don't be too sure. Very likely I'd have gone to sleep. What was it about, anyway?"

"About being prepared to meet God. The minister talked about the dangers for people in the mines: I don't think you'd have slept then. Then he said that dying was meeting God, and that after death was judgment, and—oh so much more! But Jos, if we don't get out of this, but should die down here, we shall all have to meet God, you, me and young Bobby here, and oh I wish I was ready but I'm not." His voice quivered as he said this, his position suddenly appeared so very clearly to him, and the solemnity of what he had said struck the little boy, who began to cry. It took Peter some time to quieten him and this turned the conversation aside.

The men returned, very tired, and with no success. They were all very hungry and they had another ration of food which did little to ease their pangs; the need to keep their food going as long as possible made sure that they were never full. Mercifully their water supply never failed so they were kept from thirst, which would have been very hard to bear. After their

25

poor meal, the men spent some time in prayer, which so lifted up their spirits that they suggested singing a hymn. "Come, Peter lad," said Bill Logan, "you know a good many hymns you've learnt in Sunday School. Can you think of one that will suit us?" Peter thought, then repeated:

> "Through all the changing scenes of life,
>   In trouble and in joy,
> The praises of my God shall still,
>   My heart and tongue employ."

"That'll do bravely," said Logan, "King David said 'I will bless the Lord at all times, His praise shall continually be in my mouth', and though he was never shut up in a mine, like us, I reckon he was often in as big trouble." They sang the whole of the hymn, which refreshed them, so that whenever time began to drag heavily they called on Peter to provide them with more hymns. Every now and then they struck on the roof their signal to the rescuers that they were still alive.

Thus another twenty four hours crawled by.

CHAPTER SEVEN

Death or Life Eternal?

By now the news of the accident had spread far and wide and many visitors flocked in, some out of idle curiosity, but many with a desire to help. There were rich men who paid the rescuers handsomely, to replace the wages, surgeons and doctors held themselves in readiness to help the rescuers or the rescued. Others had no money or medical skill, but only strength to lend. So many of these offered that the prisoners would soon have been released if all could have worked at the same time, but the space was so cramped that only a few could work at a time. All was busyness and bustle at the pit mouth with relays of men being taken into the mine and others coming up for rest. The anxious families hung constantly round the pit, hoping and hoping for encouraging news.

What a contrast with the five down below!

They had been shut in two days and nights and their strength was failing. The small amount of food was not enough to keep them even partially fed and now the pain of hunger was beginning to grieve them. They dare not fill themselves with what food they had left, for though they could hear the rescuers, the sounds seemed as distant as ever, and they felt they ought to reserve as much as possible in case they were called on to endure many more days. They were not as terrified as one might suppose in their circumstances. Even if they should not escape, James Freeman and Bill Logan had long ago committed themselves into the Saviour's hands and they rested there, and whilst they encouraged each other to think of the glory to come when Christ took them to their eternal rest, they were greatly concerned for the boys with them. Many times they sought to turn the boys to the Saviour; in this time of great need, they sought to show their greatest need of a Saviour's cleansing blood and the gifts of repentance and remission of sins. They spoke of the possibility of their not being rescued, of dying there, and of the quick passage of what time they had left before they might be called to stand before the judgment throne of God and give account of themselves. They all tried to sing a hymn, but their voices were beginning to crack with weakness, so they commended themselves to God's mercy and lay down to sleep.

Friday was felt to be a very solemn day in that small prison. The food was almost gone, and still the sounds of help seemed little nearer. They were very weak from long fasting, but the worst pain of hunger had passed and when they had finally eaten the last of their bread they did not feel much distress. The air was becoming stale and used up, which added to their lightheadedness, and poor little Bobby was now wandering in a dream world, he was so weak; he babbled of being in green fields and in the warmth of the sun.

Now one more trouble came to them: their lamp, which had burned dimly but steadily for three days, was at last exhausted and they were left in total darkness. Of all their troubles this seemed the worst, all others seemed bearable while there was light, now all had gone! So said the boys, but James Freeman reminded them that God had not gone, and he called them to think of the hymn which says:

"The soul that on Jesus hath leaned for repose,
He will not, He will not desert to its foes,
That soul, though all hell should endeavour to shake
He'll never, no never, no never forsake."

"My, but that's a truth to hold on to in a state like ours," said Bill Logan. "Lads, our time seems to be getting short, it is a mercy God has given us as long as this to think on eternal things. The one thing needful for you is salvation by Jesus Christ and if you haven't got that . . . We've been praying for you while we've been down here, and I don't doubt but that there's been many up top doing the same, but if anyone wants anything of God he must ask for himself, we can't get it for you. There is a Fountain filled with blood drawn from Immanuel's veins, and sinners plunged beneath that flood lose all their guilty stains." His voice died away and silence fell.

CHAPTER EIGHT

Rescue

Great commotion at the mouth of the pit! Almost before dawn a crowd had gathered hoping to hear of the rescue. The relatives of the trapped miners were waiting. They had been confidently assured that the workmen had nearly pierced the barrier and only a few more hours were needed. They were all pale and drawn with the strain, and they stood together in a silent group, no conversation left, staring each time the windlass drew up some workers from the bottom. When these said "Not yet" to the unasked question, hearts sank and lips trembled.

Down below the tension was mounting. The men worked silently, straining every muscle, and even if they had strength to spare, they had no heart to talk. True, they hoped that they were almost through, but for what purpose? For many hours there had been no

31

signals though they had strained their ears to catch the slightest chink. Had those poor souls starved, or had they been poisoned by foul gas? Bobby Lester's father was still there, though he was almost asleep with weariness, and he could no longer wield a pick.

Suddenly—a shout from one of the workmen. His long boring-rod had met with no resistance — they were through!

"Freeman, are you there?"

"Ay, and Logan and the three boys." His voice was weak and hollow, but it was a welcome sound to the rescuers.

"All living?" There was a heartbeat's silence.

"All living, thank God."

"Hear that, men, all alive!"

"Tell me again," shouted a hoarse voice, "Is my lad alive?" Even Freeman knew whose voice that was and he replied, "Ay, Bobby lives, poor little lad." Bobby Lester's father heard, and then collapsed, his endurance spent. He was carried to an open space to revive while the others turned their attention to the prisoners.

"Can you manage another hour? There's more to clear before it's safe."

"The Lord has strengthened us thus far and He will. We can wait."

Without another word, the work was resumed. Only the sound now of tools and the wheeling away of the debris. Nearer, nearer. At last the opening widened. One false move and all would be lost, not only for rescued but for the rescuers. They knew the dangers, and many silent petitions went up as they removed the last obstacles. Then the buried ones could crawl

through, dirty, haggard and blinking even in that dim light, but with gladness in their hearts and thanks- giving to Him who had delivered them from the horrible pit.

Words cannot describe the meeting of the two men and the boys with their loved ones, but a cheer rang out when Thomas Lester was drawn up, holding tightly in his arms his little Bobby, who hardly knew what was happening. The danger now arose that the starving men would be killed by kindness, and it was as well that doctors were there to see that they had only broth in small quantities until they could stand more, then they were swept home on a wave of rejoicing.

CHAPTER NINE

Prisoners Set Free

A few days later, and the everyday occupation of the mine was in full swing. The ruined galleries were restored and the miners returned to their work as if nothing had interrupted it. In a short time, the accident, though not forgotten, was scarcely mentioned. These things happened frequently, and soon passed from the front of men's minds. But there were those who could not forget. James Freeman and Bill Logan came out of that pit with their faith confirmed and strengthened, surer now than ever that their God was One to be trusted in the day of trouble and able to give joy in believing in the darkest times.

Bobby Lester, being young, soon recovered from his

trial, but he was not sent down the mine for many years. He was sent to school, his father fearing to place him in such danger again while so young, in spite of losing even his small wage.

So shaken had Jos Hartley been by his brush with death that he began a reformation of life. He began to keep holy the Sabbath day and turned his back on his former God-dishonouring ways. But more was needed than an outward show, and in time other changes were seen. He delighted to speak of what James Freeman and Bill Logan had meant to him in his time of captivity, and how they had been the means of the blessed Spirit of God leading him to seek the Lord while He is to be found and to call upon Him while He is near, to look to the Lord Jesus Christ for deliverance and to have a heart prepared to stand before the judgment throne of God, clothed in Christ's righteousness.

Life changed, too, for Peter Morrison. He returned to the mine for a short time, but after a while he and his family moved to a new part of the country where in due time, Peter was called to preach the glorious gospel of salvation by faith in Jesus Christ. He loved to recall his five days of imprisonment, starvation and danger, for it was then that the Lord had met with him, and revealed His mercy through a risen Saviour.

"Surely it was none other than the house of God, and gate of heaven to my soul—that dark dungeon down in the mine."

O. & M. Ltd.
Rugby Street
Leicester, England